£5.99

Published by

Pedigree®

Pedigree Books Limited
The Old Rectory,
Matford Lane,
Exeter, Devon
EX2 4PS

Pokémon

CONTENTS

£5.99

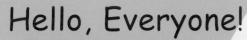

Hello, Everyone!

My name is Professor Oak, and I'd like to welcome you to the first Pokémon Official Annual! On the following pages you'll find exciting stories to read, profiles on each and every Pokémon – plus all sorts of puzzles to do! But first, here are a few important people, and things you should know about before entering the world of Pokémon!

The Pokédex is a handy device full of information and hints on training Pokémon.

Ash, Misty and Brock are your friends. They're fellow Pokémon trainers and breeders.

A young Pokémon trainer like Ash wants to win every battle, collect all 150 Pokémon – and join the ranks of the master trainers in the Pokémon League!

You can choose to be a collector like Misty, whose speciality is collecting Water Pokémon.

As a Pokémon breeder, it's Brock's job to raise the best Pokémon and to bring out their inner strength and personality.

Watch out for the enemy, Team Rocket. Jessie, James and their evil Pokémon Meowth are aiming to capture and control all rare Pokémon!

Before you can catch a Pokémon, you need a Poké Ball to put it in.

Pokémon
Gotta catch 'em all!

I CHOOSE YOU!

In the town of Pallet, Ash Ketchum could hardly control his excitement as he went to bed. Now that he was ten years old, Ash could have his own Pokémon Training Licence!

To get his licence, Ash would have to pay a visit to Professor Oak, first thing next morning. The professor would then give Ash one of three training Pokémon – Bulbasaur, Charmander or Squirtle.

All that night Ash lay awake, thinking about the wonderful journey he would soon be taking in search of Pokémon.

At last, Ash drifted into a deep sleep.

Suddenly, as if from a long way off, a bell began to ring, 'brrrrriiing-brrrrriiing'! The sound seemed to get louder and more urgent! 'BRRRRRIIING'!

"Oh, I've overslept!" cried Ash, leaping out of bed.

Ash ran all the way to Professor Oak's laboratory.

"Well, you must be Ash," said the professor's grandson Gary, who had just been to collect his first Pokémon. "Better late than never, I suppose!"

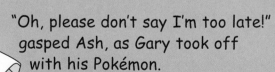

"Oh, please don't say I'm too late!" gasped Ash, as Gary took off with his Pokémon.

"Mmm, you must be Ash!" said another voice.

Ash swung round to see the professor peering down at him.

"Um, sorry I'm late, but could I have my Pokémon, professor?" asked Ash.

Taking the boy inside, Professor Oak explained that today had been a very busy day – and that meant there were no training Pokémon left!

"No Bulbasaur?" asked Ash.

The professor shook his head.

"No Charmander?"

The professor shook his head again.

"What about a Squirtle?" said Ash, now quite desperate.

"Already taken by someone who was on time, I'm afraid," said Professor Oak.

"BUT I NEED MY POKéMON!" gasped Ash.

"Well, there is one still left, but I should warn you now, there is a slight problem with this one..." began the professor.

"I'll take it!" Ash interrupted, without hesitation.

Inside the last Poké Ball, Ash found a Pokémon named Pikachu.

"It can have, well, an electrifying personality as well as power," said the professor, as Ash felt a shock shoot up his arm.

Ash set off on his journey with Pikachu. But it was hard work. Pikachu refused to go in the Poké Ball, so Ash had to pull him along.

"One day I'll be the greatest Pokémon Master in the world!" smiled Ash. "I'll soon learn how to win major battles and collect every Pokémon there is!"

I CHOOSE YOU!

While it's being trained, a Pokémon usually stays inside its Poké Ball, but Pikachu refused. He much preferred to be free.

At last, Ash stopped and said, "Okay, I'll take off my gloves – and the leash I put around you, as long as you promise not to wander off."

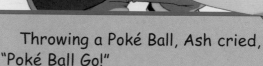

Throwing a Poké Ball, Ash cried, "Poké Ball Go!"

But the Pidgey flew away!

"You got away this time, but I have an idea," Ash called.

Resting on the branch of a tree, Pikachu just closed its eyes and yawned.

To capture a Pokémon, you usually have your own Pokémon fight with the other. But as Ash couldn't do that, he did the next best thing – or so he thought!

Picking up a rock, Ash hurled it at what he thought was another Pidgey.

"Got you this time!" laughed Ash as the rock hit its target.

But Ash had a lot to learn about the different types of Pokémon. Instead of hitting a Pidgey, he had

Suddenly, Ash and Pikachu heard a rustling sound – and saw a Pidgey sitting on a nearby rock. Ash knew that Pidgey Pokémon were easy to capture. It was a perfect target for a beginning Pokémon trainer to test his skills.

"This must be our lucky day!" laughed Ash. "We've found our first Pidgey!"

But Pikachu wasn't paying any attention.

"Please yourself!" said Ash. "I can get that Pidgey without any help from you!"

hit a Spearow! Now Spearow, unlike Pidgey, can be very bad-tempered and will attack other Pokémon and humans.

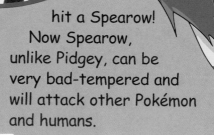

With a loud flapping of its wings, the Spearow swooped down.

Throwing himself on the ground, Ash covered his head with his hands.

Even Pikachu had to duck as the Spearow swooped to attack once again.

"What are you doing?!" yelled Ash. "Pikachu didn't throw the rock at you – I did!"

But wild Pokémon are jealous of human-trained Pokémon like Pikachu – and this ferocious bird wanted revenge!

Using its Fury Attack, the Spearow headed straight towards Pikachu!

Ash and Pikachu tried to hide in the long grass, but it was no use. Soon, more Spearow joined in, using their Peck and Growl techniques.

"Let's get out of here!" cried Ash, as he and Pikachu made a run for it.

But Spearow were hot on their trail!

Picking up Pikachu in his arms, Ash ran on and on, with Spearow still close behind.

At last, he came to the edge of a cliff.

"However will we escape now?" gasped Ash as he looked down at the sharp rocks and swirling water far below.

There was only one thing to do – JUMP!

Down, down, down, sped Ash and Pikachu, plummeting into the swirling water.

Using a fishing rod, Misty was trying to catch a Water Pokémon when she felt something tug on the end of her line.

What a surprise she had when Ash and Pikachu, attached to the end of the fishing line, shot out of the water!

"Are you alright?" asked Misty, as Ash tried to catch his breath.

Then Misty saw Pikachu – and it didn't seem to be breathing.

"Get moving! It needs a doctor!" cried Misty. "There's a Medical Centre not far from here."

I CHOOSE YOU!

With no time to lose, Ash jumped on to Misty's cycle and put Pikachu inside the basket on the front.

Peddling as fast as he could, Ash could hear Spearow getting closer all the time!

As he tried to shake off the angry birds, he lost control of the cycle.

Skidding, the cycle toppled over and Ash and Pikachu tumbled off!

"Oh, Pikachu," whispered Ash, stroking the Pokémon as it lay on the ground. "I know you don't like going inside a Poké Ball, but please trust me."

Weak and afraid, Pikachu could only watch

as Ash bravely spread his arms and called, "Are you listening, Spearow? I am destined to be the world's number one Pokémon Master – and I'm going to defeat and capture you all!"

Touched by Ash's attempt to protect it, Pikachu exerted all its remaining power, hitting the flock of Spearow with a one hundred thousand-volt electric shock!

"We're safe at last," smiled Ash, as a surviving Spearow flew away.

To show they were now true friends, Pikachu gave Ash a peck on the cheek.

"So you do like me, after all!" smiled Ash, giving Pikachu a big hug.

Glad that Pikachu now trusted him, Ash and his loyal companion continued their journey through the world of Pokémon. From now on, they would always work together.

POKÉMON MAZE

Searching for Pikachu™

Ash, Misty and Brock are searching for Pikachu in this maze. Can you show them which path to take, without having to pass other Pokémon?

SEE PAGE 63 FOR THE SOLUTION

15

POKÉMON ™

On these and the following pages, you can find out more

HEIGHT:	2 ft 4 in
WEIGHT:	15 lb
TYPE:	GRASS / POISON
ATTACKS:	SEED

#01 BULBASAUR™

This is a good Pokémon for new trainers. It's in better shape than other beginning Pokémon – which makes it more difficult to defeat and capture. At a certain time of the year, Bulbasaur gather for a festival where they evolve.

#02 IVYSAUR™

An Ivysaur has two characteristics – which means that it has twice as many strengths as many other Pokémon – and twice as many weaknesses! This Pokémon has many useful techniques, like Tackle Growl, Leech Seed and Vine Whip.

HEIGHT:	3 ft 3 in
WEIGHT:	29 lb
TYPE:	GRASS/POISON
ATTACKS:	SEED

HEIGHT:	6 ft 7 in
WEIGHT:	221 lb
TYPE:	GRASS/POISON
ATTACKS:	SEED

#03 VENUSAUR™

Although huge, Venusaur isn't totally safe from others. Fire, Poison, Flying, Dragon and Ghost are bad news for Venusaur. As its bulb grows into a flower, it gets energy from the sun. This means Venusaur must keep moving in search of sunlight.

#04 CHARMANDER™

Charmander is often given to beginning trainers. Once it gains experience, this Fire Pokémon is almost impossible to beat! Charmander is difficult to train, but with more attack power than Bulbasaur or Squirtle, it's worth it!

HEIGHT:	2 ft
WEIGHT:	19 lb
TYPE:	FIRE
ATTACKS:	LIZARD

#05 CHARMELEON™

When Charmeleon swings its burning tail, the air gets red-hot! With its special Fire Spin technique, this Pokémon can attack two to five times in a row before its enemy has a chance to respond!

HEIGHT:	3 ft 7 in
WEIGHT:	42 lb
TYPE:	FIRE
ATTACKS:	LIZARD

#06 CHARIZARD™

Charizard spits out flames that are so hot, they can melt rocks! A fully evolved lizard, it can even start a forest fire! Fire Pokémon are powerful against Ice, but they can't cope with most Water, Rock, Dragon or other Fire Pokémon.

HEIGHT:	5 ft 7 in
WEIGHT:	200 lb
TYPE:	FIRE/FLYING
ATTACKS:	LIZARD

PR⬤FILES

about your favourite Pokémon – and what they do!

#07 SQUIRTLE™

HEIGHT:	1 ft 8 in
WEIGHT:	20 lb
TYPE:	WATER
ATTACKS:	TINY TURTLE

Squirtle is another Pokémon that Professor Oak might give to a new trainer. This tiny turtle has amazing water techniques. In battle, Squirtle can spray a forceful foam from its mouth, or use the Bubble technique to slow-down an enemy.

#08 WARTORTLE™

This Pokémon has huge ears, which it uses to balance when swimming fast. An older, more experienced turtle than Squirtle, Wartortle hides in the water – and leaps out on its enemy!

HEIGHT:	3 ft 3 in
WEIGHT:	50 lb
TYPE:	WATER
ATTACKS:	TURTLE

#09 BLASTOISE™

HEIGHT:	5 ft 3 in
WEIGHT:	189 lb
TYPE:	WATER
ATTACKS:	SHELLFISH

Blastoise has a hard shell that hides two high-pressure water cannons, capable of pumping out hundreds of gallons of water every minute! Blastoise uses its cannons for extra fast tackles.

#10 CATERPIE™

Caterpie has short feet with suction cups on the ends that allow it to climb walls and trees without getting tired. Once it changes into a Metapod, it can no longer move; some trainers prefer to slow Caterpie's evolution and build up its experience.

HEIGHT:	1 ft
WEIGHT:	6 lb
TYPE:	BUG
ATTACKS:	WORM

#11 METAPOD™

HEIGHT:	2 ft 4 in
WEIGHT:	22 lb
TYPE:	BUG
ATTACKS:	COCOON

Metapod has only a short time before it evolves into a Butterfree. Like a caterpillar in a cocoon, Metapod can't move. Its tender body needs protecting from bird enemies like Pidgey and Spearow.

#12 BUTTERFREE™

This Bug Pokémon makes the most of its ability to fly. Flapping its wings at great speed, the beautiful but dangerous Butterfree fills the air with toxic dust!

HEIGHT:	3 ft 7 in
WEIGHT:	71 lb
TYPE:	BUG/FLYING
ATTACKS:	BUTTERFLY

HEIGHT:	1 ft
WEIGHT:	7 lb
TYPE:	BUG/POISON
ATTACKS:	HAIRY BUG

#13 WEEDLE™

Weedle is usually found in forests, munching on leaves. With only Poison Sting and String Shot techniques to help it in battle, this Pokémon's powers are limited – but powerful! Like Caterpie, Weedle's String Shot slows down its enemy.

#14 KAKUNA™

Kakuna, like Metapod, is unable to move and can't attack. With no techniques, its only defence is to harden its shell. Kakuna needs a lot of care during this stage, but it will soon shed its cocoon and evolve into a Beedrill!

HEIGHT:	2 ft
WEIGHT:	22 lb
TYPE:	BUG/POISON
ATTACKS:	COCOON

HEIGHT:	3 ft 3 in
WEIGHT:	65 lb
TYPE:	BUG/POISON
ATTACKS:	POISON BEE

#15 BEEDRILL™

Beedrill attacks enemies using the large, poisonous stingers on its front legs and tail. It has been a dangerous process, but this former Weedle is now extremely strong and fast!

#16 PIDGEY™

Pidgey is the easiest bird to capture. Found in forests and wooded areas, this bird flaps its wings as hard as it can to kick up sand and dust to blind enemies. Its Gust power enables Pidgey to create huge tornadoes.

HEIGHT:	1 ft
WEIGHT:	4 lb
TYPE:	NORMAL/FLYING
ATTACKS:	TINY BIRD

HEIGHT:	3 ft 7 in
WEIGHT:	66 lb
TYPE:	NORMAL/FLYING
ATTACKS:	BIRD

#17 PIDGEOTTO™

This Pokémon has learned a few more techniques as it's evolved. Using its Gust technique, a Pidgeotto can blow away almost anyone – or anything – that gets in its path! The heavyweight Pidgeotto is very protective of its territory.

#18 PIDGEOT™

Now evolved into its final stage, Pidgeot is even sharper and faster than Pidgeotto. It can fly up to two miles above ground – and faster than the speed of sound! When hunting, Pidgeot fly just above the water's surface to catch Fish.

HEIGHT:	4 ft 11 in
WEIGHT:	87 lb
TYPE:	NORMAL/FLYING
ATTACKS:	BIRD

PROFILES

#19 RATTATA™

HEIGHT:	1 ft
WEIGHT:	8 lb
TYPE:	NORMAL
ATTACKS:	RAT

Rattata are very common. They may be small, but they're extremely fast! Using their sharp teeth, these Pokémon will bite anything in an attack. Surprisingly, they live in peace and harmony with Pidgey.

#20 RATICATE™

Raticate use their whiskers for guidance and to maintain balance. Without the use of whiskers, Raticate are very slow. The Hyper Fang technique, that Rattata and Raticate both share, is so frightening that enemies are afraid to attack back!

HEIGHT:	2 ft 4 in
WEIGHT:	41 lb
TYPE:	NORMAL
ATTACKS:	RAT

#21 SPEAROW™

This bird may be small, but it has a terrible temper. The Spearow's Fury Attack is definitely something to see! But Spearow has to flap its short wings extremely hard to stay in the air, which can be very hard work.

HEIGHT:	1 ft
WEIGHT:	4 lb
TYPE:	NORMAL/FLYING
ATTACKS:	TINY BIRD

#22 FEAROW™

Unlike Spearow, Fearow has huge wings, which means it can stay in the air for a long time without stopping to rest. At higher experience levels, this Pokémon is able to use its Mirror Move technique to copy an enemy's attack.

HEIGHT:	3 ft 11 in
WEIGHT:	84 lb
TYPE:	NORMAL/FLYING
ATTACKS:	BEAK

#23 EKANS™

HEIGHT:	6 ft 7 in
WEIGHT:	15 lb
TYPE:	POISON
ATTACKS:	SNAKE

Ekans is one of Team Rocket's favourite Pokémon to use in battle! Spelled backwards, this cunning fighter's name reads 'snake'! If you're a new trainer, beware – Ekans will have you on your toes!

#24 ARBOK™

Arbok is even more dangerous than Ekans! There's a rumour going around that the warning marks on this Pokémon's belly vary on different parts of its body. To paralyse an attacker, Arbok uses its Glare technique.

HEIGHT:	11 ft 6 in
WEIGHT:	143 lb
TYPE:	POISON
ATTACKS:	COBRA

POKéMON

HEIGHT:	1 ft 4 in
WEIGHT:	13 lb
TYPE:	ELECTRIC
ATTACKS:	MOUSE

#25 PIKACHU™

Pikachu can zap an opponent with its electric power, just by squeezing its cheeks! Team Rocket is always trying to capture this rare Pokémon. But too many in the same place can cause lightning storms in nearby cities!

#26 RAICHU™

This powerful Pokémon uses its 10,000-volt Thunder Wave technique to paralyse enemies. Raichu has so much electrical power in its body that it has to use its tail as an earth to avoid shocking itself!

HEIGHT:	2 ft 7 in
WEIGHT:	66 lb
TYPE:	ELECTRIC
ATTACKS:	MOUSE

HEIGHT:	2 ft
WEIGHT:	26 lb
TYPE:	GROUND
ATTACKS:	MOUSE

#27 SANDSHREW™

Sandshrew make good pets if you happen to live near a desert. But they are also pretty tough to train because most of them are fussy eaters. These Pokémon burrow deep underground in hot, dry places.

#28 SANDSLASH™

Sandslash can make life difficult for its enemies. When threatened, it curls into a ball, using the spines on its back to protect it from predators. With the Fury Swipe technique, Sandslash can attack two to five times in a row!

HEIGHT:	3 ft 3 in
WEIGHT:	65 lb
TYPE:	GROUND
ATTACKS:	MOUSE

HEIGHT:	1 ft 4 in
WEIGHT:	15 lb
TYPE:	POISON
ATTACKS:	POISON PIN

#29 NIDORAN™ ♀

Here's a good Pokémon to have when battling against Grass or Bug Pokémon. This Nidoran has small, poisonous barbs that make it extremely dangerous!

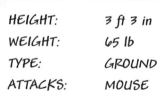

#30 NIDORINA™

Nidorina does not evolve by gaining experience. To turn it into a Nidoqueen, you need a Moon Stone. In an attack, a Double Kick or Tail Whip soon stops an opponent! Nidorina's horns grow slowly, so it likes to use its teeth and claws.

HEIGHT:	2 ft 7 in
WEIGHT:	44 lb
TYPE:	POISON
ATTACKS:	POISON PIN

#31 NIDOQUEEN™

HEIGHT:	4 ft 3 in
WEIGHT:	132 lb
TYPE:	POISON/GROUND
ATTACKS:	DRILL

Nidoqueen prefers to use its powerful tail in battle. Because of its great weight, this Pokémon takes advantage of its size for strong attacks like the Body Slam. It is protected by the hard scales on its body.

#32 NIDORAN™ ♂

This Nidoran has ears that quickly stiffen at the first sign of danger! Take care, because the barbs on its head release a powerful poison. Although a pretty lightweight Pokémon, it can give as good as it gets in many situations.

HEIGHT:	1 ft 8 in
WEIGHT:	20 lb
TYPE:	POISON
ATTACKS:	POISON PIN

#33 NIDORINO™

HEIGHT:	2 ft 11 in
WEIGHT:	43 lb
TYPE:	POISON
ATTACKS:	POISON PIN

Nidorino often uses Focus Energy to increase its power before attacking – but that takes time. Enemies can use the pause to attack before Nidorino is ready! The horn on its head contains a strong poison.

#34 NIDOKING™

Nidoking is a powerful warrior – and not to be messed with. Wrapping its strong tail around 'prey', it quickly crushes the enemy's bones! Nidoking also has a few other useful techniques: Tackle, Horn Attack, Poison Sting and Thrash.

HEIGHT:	4 ft 7 in
WEIGHT:	137 lb
TYPE:	POISON
ATTACKS:	POISON PIN

#35 CLEFAIRY™

HEIGHT:	2 ft
WEIGHT:	17 lb
TYPE:	NORMAL
ATTACKS:	FAIRY

Admired for its magical powers, this rare, peaceful fairy is hard to find. Clefairy has a special Metronome technique that allows it to attack in various ways. Some people believe the Clefairy have formed their own society inside Mt. Moon.

#36 CLEFABLE™

This is one of the rarest Pokémon in the world! To turn a Clefairy into a Clefable, you need a Moon Stone. However, once changed, it cannot learn new techniques. The moment it knows people are around, this shy fairy will run and hide!

HEIGHT:	4 ft 3 in
WEIGHT:	88 lb
TYPE:	NORMAL
ATTACKS:	FAIRY

POKéMON

#37 VULPIX™

HEIGHT:	2 ft
WEIGHT:	22 lb
TYPE:	FIRE
ATTACKS:	FOX

Vulpix looks sweet – but looks can be deceiving! Behind its soft exterior this rare Pokémon has an inner-strength. As Vulpix grows older, its tail splits at the tip. Vulpix can then use the Fire Spin technique to block an opponent from moving.

#38 NINETALES™

Ninetales likes plotting revenge against its enemies. The only way to add this Pokémon to your team is to carefully raise a Vulpix, then use a Fire Stone to evolve it.

HEIGHT:	3 ft 7 in
WEIGHT:	44 lb
TYPE:	FIRE
ATTACKS:	FOX

#39 JIGGLYPUFF™

HEIGHT:	1 ft 8 in
WEIGHT:	12 lb
TYPE:	NORMAL
ATTACKS:	BALLOON

The rare Jigglypuff uses its Sing Attack to soothe even the toughest of enemies into dreamland – then it finishes off with a good pounding! To find a mysterious Jigglypuff, you must search the long grass outside Mt. Moon.

#40 WIGGLYTUFF™

To show that it's angry, this Pokémon sucks in air and inflates its soft rubbery body like a huge balloon. Like Jigglypuff, it uses the Sing Attack against enemies. Wigglytuff also has an extremely fierce Doubleslap and Defence Curl technique.

HEIGHT:	3 ft 3 in
WEIGHT:	26 lb
TYPE:	NORMAL
ATTACKS:	BALLOON

#41 ZUBAT™

HEIGHT:	2 ft 7 in
WEIGHT:	17 lb
TYPE:	POISON/FLYING
ATTACKS:	BAT

Zubat live in groups and use ultrasonic waves (a built-in radar system) to move around in the dark. Using the Leech Life technique, Zubat can suck all the energy out of an enemy, thereby increasing their own energy.

#42 GOLBAT™

Golbat also feeds on victims' energy. Fully evolved, it uses sharp fangs to drain a horrendous 48 cubic inches of blood per bite! To confuse opponents, Golbat will use the Haze technique so enemies can't tell if it's friend or foe.

HEIGHT:	5 ft 3 in
WEIGHT:	121 lb
TYPE:	POISON/FLYING
ATTACKS:	BAT

HEIGHT:	5 ft 7 in
WEIGHT:	169 lb
TYPE:	WATER
ATTACKS:	DUCK

#55 GOLDUCK™

Golduck is a graceful fighter both on land and in the water. This large yet extremely elegant Water Pokémon enjoys swimming by lakeshores.

#56 MANKEY™

Mankey can lose its temper at the drop of a hat! This Pokémon can be calm and in complete control one minute – and hopping mad the next! As a Fighting Pokémon, Mankey is more agile than most.

HEIGHT:	1 ft 8 in
WEIGHT:	62 lb
TYPE:	FIGHTING
ATTACKS:	PIG MONKEY

HEIGHT:	3 ft 3 in
WEIGHT:	71 lb
TYPE:	FIGHTING
ATTACKS:	PIG MONKEY

#57 PRIMEAPE™

Primeape has a rather impressive Karate Chop technique – as some of its enemies have discovered! Another Fighting Pokémon, Primeape refuses to give up until it has caught an opponent.

#58 GROWLITHE™

This puppy Pokémon is extremely rare. If threatened, it will bark and bite to scare intruders. A Fire Pokémon, it's good against enemies such as Grass, Ice and Bug Pokémon. Growlithe is very protective of its territory – and its owner.

HEIGHT:	2 ft 4 in
WEIGHT:	42 lb
TYPE:	FIRE
ATTACKS:	PUPPY

HEIGHT:	6 ft 3 in
WEIGHT:	342 lb
TYPE:	FIRE
ATTACKS:	LEGENDARY

#59 ARCANINE™

Arcanine runs so fast and smoothly, it looks like it's flying! This Fire Pokémon makes a very loyal pet if trained well. Arcanine's beauty has been admired by other Pokémon for centuries.

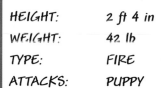

#60 POLIWAG™

As Poliwag has newly grown legs and no arms, it finds swimming the easiest way to travel. Poliwag has a great Hypnosis and Body Slam technique that comes in useful against many Fire, Ground and Rock Pokémon.

HEIGHT:	2 ft
WEIGHT:	27 lb
TYPE:	WATER
ATTACKS:	TADPOLE

POKÉMON™

#61 POLIWHIRL™

HEIGHT:	3 ft 3 in
WEIGHT:	44 lb
TYPE:	WATER
ATTACKS:	TADPOLE

Unlike Poliwag, Poliwhirl can live happily in or out of the water. Out of water, it sweats to keep its body slimy. Poliwhirl uses a variety of mind powers, like Amnesia, to make it more powerful.

#62 POLIWRATH™

This Pokémon has outstanding swimming abilities. Using the Water Stone, once Poliwrath has evolved, it will take on more fighting techniques, like Body Slam. But it can still use Hypnosis to soothe an enemy to sleep.

HEIGHT:	4 ft 3 in
WEIGHT:	119 lb
TYPE:	WATER/FIGHTING
ATTACKS:	TADPOLE

#63 ABRA™

HEIGHT:	2 ft 11 in
WEIGHT:	43 lb
TYPE:	PSYCHIC
ATTACKS:	PSYCHIC

Abra is able to read minds, which often comes in useful when in combat. Sensing danger, Abra can move itself – by thought – to another place! To capture Abra, try paralysing it before it runs away.

#64 KADABRA™

Kadabra likes to use its strong mind instead of its strong body to win competitions. This Psychic Pokémon sends out special brainwaves that give headaches to anyone who gets too close.

HEIGHT:	4 ft 3 in
WEIGHT:	125 lb
TYPE:	PSYCHIC
ATTACKS:	PSYCHIC

#65 ALAKAZAM™

HEIGHT:	4 ft 11 in
WEIGHT:	106 lb
TYPE:	PSYCHIC
ATTACKS:	PSYCHIC

Alakazam is even smarter than a super-computer! With an I.Q. of 5,000, it's an absolute genius! This brainy psychic Pokémon has some mind-blowing techniques like Psybeam, Confusion and Disable to ward off enemies.

#66 MACHOP™

This Pokémon loves to study all kinds of martial arts, which can make it very dangerous, indeed! Quick and mobile, Machop can even avoid most special techniques. An intelligent Pokémon, it makes a great teacher and friend.

HEIGHT:	2 ft 7 in
WEIGHT:	43 lb
TYPE:	FIGHTING
ATTACKS:	SUPERPOWER

PROFILES

#67 MACHOKE™

HEIGHT:	4 ft 1 in
WEIGHT:	155 lb
TYPE:	FIGHTING
ATTACKS:	SUPERPOWER

Sometimes Machoke is so busy admiring itself in the mirror, it forgets to do any training! But that doesn't cause too many problems – Machoke is so strong, it has to wear a special 'power-save' belt to control its movements.

#68 MACHAMP™

The incredibly strong Machamp has to be traded before it can evolve. With the bonus of extra arms, this Pokémon gives punches that can send a challenger to the Moon!

HEIGHT:	5 ft 3 in
WEIGHT:	287 lb
TYPE:	FIGHTING
ATTACKS:	SUPERPOWER

#69 BELLSPROUT™

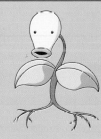

HEIGHT:	2 ft 4 in
WEIGHT:	9 lb
TYPE:	GRASS/POISON
ATTACKS:	FLOWER

Bellsprout traps and eats bugs, just like a Venus flytrap! To catch this plant-type Pokémon, it's best to use your most powerful technique before it has time to use its Growth technique against you!

#70 WEEPINBELL™

Weepinbell, like its cousin Bellsprout, likes to start off a battle using its Growth technique – and swiftly follows with a dose of Poison Powder. Then all it takes is one spray of acid from this flycatcher Pokémon – and the fight is over!

HEIGHT:	3 ft 3 in
WEIGHT:	14 lb
TYPE:	GRASS/POISON
ATTACKS:	FLYCATCHER

#71 VICTREEBEL™

HEIGHT:	5 ft 7 in
WEIGHT:	34 lb
TYPE:	GRASS/POISON
ATTACKS:	FLYCATCHER

There's a rumour going around that Victreebel live in groups in the jungle. With a Leaf Stone, you may be able to evolve a Victreebel, which can use its Poison Powder, Sleep Powder or Wrap technique to see off an enemy.

#72 TENTACOOL™

Tentacool can be found floating in warm, shallow water, where the temperature is a constant 78°C . This jellyfish has a beautiful red spot on its head called 'the ruby of the sea'. Keep an eye on its poisonous stingers!

HEIGHT:	2 ft 11 in
WEIGHT:	100 lb
TYPE:	WATER/POISON
ATTACKS:	JELLYFISH

POKÉMON PROFILES

#73 TENTACRUEL™

HEIGHT:	5 ft 3 in
WEIGHT:	121 lb
TYPE:	WATER/POISON
ATTACKS:	JELLYFISH

Tentacruel has at least twelve new stinger-tipped tentacles! So, there's no need to tell you that its sting is vicious! This Pokémon is a heavyweight jellyfish not to be reckoned with.

#74 GEODUDE™

Geodude has a tough, rock-like skin that makes it almost impossible to attack – or capture. It's found in fields and mountains, although you could easily think it's a rock and miss it! Unless you annoy Geodude, it probably won't even move!

HEIGHT:	1 ft 4 in
WEIGHT:	44 lb
TYPE:	ROCK/GROUND
ATTACKS:	ROCK

#75 GRAVELER™

HEIGHT:	3 ft 3 in
WEIGHT:	232 lb
TYPE:	ROCK/GROUND
ATTACKS:	ROCK

Graveler will roll over anything that gets in its path. As it evolves, its hard, rocky skin grows layers of sharp scales. Graveler's various techniques, like Tackle and Earthquake, are very impressive!

#76 GOLEM™

Golem is easier to spot than Geodude or Graveler. Once a year, it sheds its bedrock shell and gets even bigger! A Graveler must be traded with a friend in order to evolve into a Golem.

HEIGHT:	4 ft 7 in
WEIGHT:	622 lb
TYPE:	ROCK/GROUND
ATTACKS:	MEGATON

#77 PONYTA™

HEIGHT:	3 ft 3 in
WEIGHT:	66 lb
TYPE:	FIRE
ATTACKS:	FIRE HORSE

Ponyta would never use its flaming tail to burn anyone it trusted. Its hooves are ten times stronger than diamonds, and can trample anything flat in seconds. Ponyta are great racers and love to jump.

#78 RAPIDASH™

Just as its name suggests, Rapidash is very fast! It likes nothing more than to chase anything that moves, in the hope of racing it. So you might have trouble catching this speedy Pokémon.

HEIGHT:	5 ft 7 in
WEIGHT:	209 lb
TYPE:	FIRE
ATTACKS:	FIRE HORSE

Pokémon
WORDSEARCH

Find and circle the names below in the grid – vertically, horizontally or diagonally. The letters left over spell another Pokémon. What is it?

```
D R A Z I R A H C
B L A S T O I S E
U E C B P L H Q M
L E E A R T F U U
B S R A W A K I H
A A K O B R A R C
S P E A R O W T A
A M O O L G I L K
U G O L B A T E I
R R Y Y E G D I P
```

_ _ _ _ _ _ _ _

ABRA	GLOOM	PIDGEY
ARBOK	GOLBAT	PIKACHU
BLASTOISE	MEOWTH	SEEL
BULBASAUR	MUK	SPEAROW
CHARIZARD	PARAS	SQUIRTLE

FOR THE SOLUTION, TURN TO PAGE 63

29

POKÉMON

Gotta catch 'em all!

BULBASAUR™ AND THE HIDDEN VILLAGE

Ash, Misty and Brock were lost. As they tried to decide which way to go, the friends saw something move in the bushes.

"It's a Pokémon!" said Ash.

"Oddish! This Pokémon is typically found roaming the forest, scattering pollen as it walks around," stated Ash's Pokédex.

Taking out a Poké Ball, Misty said, "Go, Starmie! Water Gun now!"

As Oddish weakened under Starmie's attack, Misty threw the Poké Ball to catch it – and missed!

"Looks like we've got more company!" said Ash, pointing to a Bulbasaur.

"Bulbasaur! It buries the seed of a plant on its back from birth," said the Pokédex. "The seed slowly develops. Researchers are unsure whether to classify Bulbasaur

as a plant or an animal. Bulbasaur are extremely tough and difficult to capture in the wild!"

Using its Tackle technique, Bulbasaur soon put Starmie out of action.

"Now it's my turn to try. Bulbasaur is mine!" exclaimed Ash, throwing a Poké Ball. "Butterfree, I choose you!"

Butterfree used its Sleep Powder attack, but it was no match for Bulbasaur's Poison Powder attack.

"Hang in there!" said Ash, as his Butterfree fell to the ground.

But Bulbasaur was already running back into the forest.

"I bet there are Bulbasaur all over this place," said Ash, as they crossed a rickety wooden bridge.

Then, just as Brock said, "This place doesn't even appear on my map!"

the bridge collapsed and they all fell!

Ash and Misty managed to cling to some rocks, but Brock tumbled into the river.

"Ash, you have to pull us up!" gasped Misty.

With his last ounce of strength, Ash managed to pull himself and Misty to safety.

Now the pair had to find Brock. But they had only gone a short distance when...

"This is not our day!" said Ash, as he and Misty fell into a huge hole below! Once again, Ash and Misty managed to escape.

"I think we should go this way," said Misty, pointing to a wooded area.

The two friends hadn't gone far when Misty caught her foot in a rope. It was another trap!

A net dropped down from a tree – and swished them into the air!

BULBASAUR AND THE HIDDEN VILLAGE

Meanwhile, Team Rocket wasn't far away!

"The village we're looking for should be on the other side of that bridge," said Jessie.

"Let's hope the rumours are true!" added James, looking through his binoculars.

"Perhaps Brock's been washed out to the ocean!" said Ash, worriedly.

"Any particular reason why you're hanging around in that net?" said a voice.

Ash and Misty looked down to see Brock grinning back at them.

After setting them free, Brock explained that as the current was carrying him away, a girl came to his rescue.

Leading Ash and Misty to a nearby clearing, Brock introduced them to Melanie.

Ash and Misty could hardly believe their eyes. There were Pokémon everywhere!

"This is a place where Pokémon are able to rest. When Pokémon get injured or are abandoned by their trainers, they can come here," explained Brock. "Melanie takes care of them until they feel better."

"I wonder who set all the traps around here?" said Ash.

"I have to protect the injured Pokémon, so I set the traps to catch trainers before they try to capture the Pokémon," said Melanie.

As they crossed the nearby bridge, Team Rocket were already planning what they would do with all the Pokémon they captured.

Suddenly, the frayed ropes snapped – and Team Rocket fell towards the rocks!

THUD! CRACK! THWACK! All three hit the rocks, then plummeted into the water!

"Are your traps strong enough to keep robbers out of this place?" asked Ash.

Before Melanie could answer, the friends heard a crashing sound coming from a little way off in the forest.

"This is the third hole we've fallen into!" cried Jessie. "How come nobody ever falls into our traps, but we always fall into theirs?!"

"I'm sorry if we frightened you," Misty told the Oddish they had seen earlier.

When Bulbasaur saw Misty approaching Oddish, it thought she meant to harm the

Pokémon – and attacked!

"Let's see how tough you really are, Bulbasaur!" said Ash, taking out a Poké Ball.

"Bulbasaur was only protecting Oddish," said Melanie. "Bulbasaur volunteered to guard our village. It protects the injured Pokémon whenever

Just then, Team Rocket floated into view, hovering high above the village.

"I congratulate myself for this brilliant scheme!" grinned James.

"I suggested tying the balloons on the stadium roof!" said Meowth.

Landing near Ash and his friends, Jessie announced,

enemies try to attack them."

"So that's why Bulbasaur tried to attack me!" said Misty. "It thought I was going to hurt Oddish!"

"Bulbasaur is so brave," said Ash. "It would be great to have a Pokémon like that!"

"Today, only at Jessie's stadium – it's the Team Rocket Pokémon Challenge!"

"Step right up!" called James, as a long hose appeared from the stadium – and began sucking up everything around!

BULBASAUR AND THE HIDDEN VILLAGE

"Run for cover!" cried Ash.

Everyone ran, but poor Oddish wasn't fast enough, and it was sucked towards the stadium!

Using its handy Vine Whip technique, Bulbasaur scooped little Oddish to safety.

"That rotten little pest! He's always ruining our flawless plans!" cried Jessie.

"Not this time. He's gathered them all in one place for us!" grinned James.

"Pidgeotto! I choose you!" called Ash, throwing a Poké Ball. "Pidgeotto! Gust attack!"

The bird-like Pokémon whipped up a huge tornado that blasted Team Rocket far, far away!

"Ash, I think Bulbasaur should go with you," said Melanie, a little later. "This village is too small and the bulb on its back can't grow. Bulbasaur needs to go out in the world - and I know you'll take good care of it."

"Well, if you really want me to," said Ash, hardly able to contain his excitement.

"Bulbasaur will join you on one condition," smiled Melanie. "It wants to battle you in a Pokémon match!"

"If you want a match, you'll get it!" said Ash.

Bulbasaur and Ash's Pikachu Pokémon faced each other and prepared to battle.

Pikachu managed to dodge Bulbasaur's Vine Whip attack, but its Tackle technique sent little Pikachu flying through the air!

"Pikachu! Thunder Shock attack!" called Ash. Squeezing its cheeks, Pikachu sent out a burst of electric power that knocked Bulbasaur off its feet!

"All right! Poké Ball go!" cried Ash, catching the dazed Bulbasaur as it lay on the ground.

"I've been thinking," said Brock. "I wouldn't mind staying and helping you out, Melanie."

"That's very kind of you, but I wouldn't want to keep you

from all your wonderful adventures," said Melanie.

"I suppose you're right," said Brock, trying hard not to blush.

"Don't worry Bulbasaur, you'll see your friends again," said Ash. "As soon as they feel well enough, they'll leave the village, too."

Later, Misty couldn't resist teasing Brock. "So what did Melanie say when you said you loved her, Brock? Did you kiss her goodbye?"

"Would you please stop embarrassing me!" pleaded Brock, as he gave Misty a playful swipe.

48   49   50   51

47   46   45

28   29   30

31

27   26   25

FIRST TO FINISH!

Ash, Misty and Brock want to find a rare Tangela. To play this game with a friend, place your different coloured counters on 'Start'. Take turns to roll dice and move around the board. If you land on a picture, do what the 'key' tells you. The first to Tangela gets to keep it!

24

23   22   21

12

11

10

1

Start

36

52
53
54
Finish

44
43
42
41
40

32
33
37
36
34
39
38
35

= Take an extra turn
= Go back to start
= Go on 2 spaces
- Miss a turn
= Go back 2 spaces

20
19
18
17
16

13
14
15

9
8
7
6
5

2
3
4

37

POKÉMON
SHADOWS

First match the shadows with the Pokémon they belong to, then rearrange the letters to spell their names.

GLEDONE

....

CUPHIKA

....

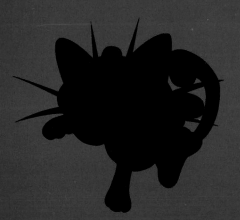

RUBLASUBA

....

UETETFREBR

....

WOTHEM

....

TILQUERS

....

SEE PAGE 63 FOR THE SOLUTION

POKéMON
Gotta catch 'em all !

CHARMANDER™
THE STRAY POKéMON!

With Bulbasaur as his newest Pokémon, Ash and his friends headed for Vermillion City. But finding Vermillion wasn't easy! While trying to figure out exactly where they were, something caught their eye.

'It's a Charmander!' said Brock.

'Charmander. A flame burns on the tip of its tail from birth,' said Ash's Pokédex. 'It is said that a Charmander dies if its flame ever goes out.'

'It looks like it's in bad shape,' said Misty.

'Catch it and we'll take it to a Pokémon Centre for help,' suggested Brock.

'Poké Ball Go!' cried Ash.

But the Charmander stayed on a rock, whining pitifully.

'Look at the flame on its tail,' said Brock. 'It could still have the strength to battle. Try one more time, Ash.'

'Pika! Pika!' said Pikachu.

'I think Pikachu is trying to tell us that Charmander's waiting for somebody,' said Ash.

'Then we'd better leave it,' said Brock. 'It's best if its own trainer takes care of it.'

As they arrived at a Pokémon Centre, Ash and his friends heard some boys talking.

'You've got a cool Pokémon collection, Damian,' said one boy.

'I thought you had a Charmander as well,' said another boy.

'I had one, but it was so weak, it couldn't even beat the weakest opponents!' said Damian.

'Charmander may be weak against Water Pokémon, but if their trainers work hard, they can be strong,' Brock told Ash and Misty.

'So what did you do with the Charmander?' said Damian's friend.

'I left it on a rock and promised I'd come back for it later,' Damian laughed.

Brock was furious when he heard what Damian had done. 'You lied to your Pokémon, now it's waiting out there in the rain for you!'

'What I do is none of your business!' said Damian.

'Pika pika,' cried Pikachu.

'You want to fight me?' Damian said to Pikachu.

Before the argument got any worse, Joy arrived to calm things down. 'Break it up! You know the rules!' she said. 'Pokémon are never to be used in personal fights. It is disrespectful to both the Pokémon and their trainers!'

Damian and his friend left, leaving Ash, Brock and Misty to worry about Charmander.

The friends staggered through a nasty storm to rescue the abandoned Pokémon.

'The flame on Charmander's tail is almost out!' said Ash.

'Let's get it back to the Pokémon Centre,' said Brock.

As soon as they arrived at the Centre, Joy examined the Pokémon. 'Charmander is very weak,' she said. 'How could you let it get like this?'

'It's not our fault!' exclaimed Ash.

'Damian's the one who abandoned it!'

At last, using just the right medicines, Joy announced that Charmander would make a complete recovery.

Leaving Charmander to rest, Ash, Brock and Misty fell asleep.

41

CHARMANDER™ THE STRAY POKÉMON!

'Wake up!' cried Brock. 'Charmander's disappeared!'

'I bet it went back to wait for Damian!' said Ash.

'It's no use trying to find Charmander again,' said Misty. 'We can't force it to come with us if it wants to wait for Damian.'

'Misty is right. There's nothing we can do until Charmander realises the truth!' said Joy.

'Come on!' said Misty. 'Let's head for Vermillion.'

Meanwhile, the evil Team Rocket were lying in wait!

'Finally,' said James, 'a fool-proof plan to capture Pikachu!'

'I can't wait to test our new Automatic, High-speed, Super-duper, Watchamacallit!' laughed Jessie.

'Not another hole driller!' said Meowth. 'We tried that already.'

'If at first you don't succeed...' puffed Jessie, as she and James drilled a huge hole in the ground.

Covering the hole with branches and twigs, Team Rocket hid – and waited!

As Ash and his friends walked by, the branches snapped.

'Our invention worked!' said Jessie, as Ash, Brock, Misty and Pikachu all fell into the hole.

'You belong to us now, Pikachu!' said James. Pikachu puffed out its cheeks and zapped Jessie and James with a powerful bolt of electricity! But Jessie only laughed, 'Rubber will not conduct electricity – and we're wearing our anti-Pikachu rubber suits!'

As Pikachu tried to run away, James called, 'Our anti-Pikachu Rubber Balloon Bazooka!'

'Ready, aim, fire!' called Jessie. Pikachu was trapped!

'Hello, down there!' called Jessie, as she and James looked down at Ash, Brock and Misty.

'Don't worry! Pikachu is safe with us!' laughed James.

Just then, Charmander appeared!

'What is that thing saying?' asked Jessie, as Charmander gave several squeaks.

'It's ordering you to give Pikachu back!' said Meowth.

'What's wrong with dumping a weak Pokémon!' said Damian. 'I wasn't going to come back, but now that I've seen what it can do, I'm glad I did!'

'Damian doesn't care about you, Charmander. He just wants to use you to win matches!' said Misty.

'That does it!' yelled Damian. 'I'll crush you with every Pokémon I've got!'

But then Pikachu and Charmander used their Electric and Fire and techniques to chase Damian away.

'Step aside, you insolent little firebug!' said James.

Using its Fire attack, Charmander sent a burst of flames spinning through the air!

'Didn't I tell you we needed fire-proof uniforms?' sighed James.

'Shut up – and keep running!' puffed Jessie.

'Charmander knew we cared. That's why it's here,' smiled Misty.

Just then Damian turned up, looking for his Pokémon. 'Charmander is mine!' he shouted.

'But you abandoned it!' said Ash.

Afterwards, Brock said that Ash should be the one to keep Charmander, 'It will be a great Pokémon, and you deserve it.'

'Thank you, Brock,' said Ash. 'Welcome to the group, Charmander!'

And so, Charmander joined Ash and his friends on their journey.

POKéMON

#79 SLOWPOKE™

HEIGHT:	3 ft 11 in
WEIGHT:	79 lb
TYPE:	WATER/PSYCHIC
ATTACKS:	DOPEY

This Pokémon simply dips its tail in the ocean and waits for a Shellder to bite – then it's instant Slowbro! Slowpoke, unlike Ponyta and Rapidash, doesn't like to move. But its Confusion technique manages to put some Pokémon in a spin!

#80 SLOWBRO™

Slowbro are cute hermit crabs whose luck and good instincts are often useful. Although they're slow mentally and physically, these Pokémon make good pets – as long as you have patience when teaching them new techniques.

HEIGHT:	5 ft 3 in
WEIGHT:	173 lb
TYPE:	WATER/PSYCHIC
ATTACKS:	HERMIT CRAB

#81 MAGNEMITE™

HEIGHT:	1 ft
WEIGHT:	13 lb
TYPE:	ELECTRIC
ATTACKS:	MAGNET

Appearing from nowhere, its antigravity skill enables Magnemite to float in the air. Good at finding small metal objects, this Pokémon uses Thunder Wave and other almost unbeatable shocking techniques to attack opponents.

#82 MAGNETON™

Magneton are three Magnemites joined together. When dark sunspots appear on the Sun, Magneton attack more often! Electric, Grass and Dragon Pokémon don't have much to worry about, but Water and Flying Pokémon need to take care!

HEIGHT:	3 ft 3 in
WEIGHT:	132 lb
TYPE:	ELECTRIC
ATTACKS:	MAGNET

#83 FARFETCH'D™

HEIGHT:	2 ft 7 in
WEIGHT:	33 lb
TYPE:	NORMAL/FLYING
ATTACKS:	WILD DUCK

This Pokémon is very rare, but there is a trader in Vermillion City who will give you Farfetch'd in exchange for a Spearow! With its Swords Dance technique, Farfetch'd uses sprigs of green onion as mini-swords to attack enemies!

#84 DODUO™

Doduo have huge feet that leave massive prints in the ground, making it easy for an enemy to spot them! Although these twin-headed birds can't fly well, they are extremely fast and have some fierce techniques like Fury Attack and Rage!

HEIGHT:	4 ft 7 in
WEIGHT:	86 lb
TYPE:	NORMAL/FLYING
ATTACKS:	TWIN BIRD

PR⚬FILES

#85 DODRIO™

Dodrio has three heads - one for joy, one for sorrow - and a third for anger! This super-smart bird invents complicated plans to win battles. You won't catch Dodrio off-guard, because while two of its heads sleep, one always stays awake!

HEIGHT:	5 ft 11 in
WEIGHT:	188 lb
TYPE:	NORMAL/FLYING
ATTACKS:	TRIPLE BIRD

#86 SEEL™

As long as you can stand the cold, this Pokémon makes a lovable friend. Seel lives in the icy Arctic and uses the hard horn on its head to smash its way through ice. Head Butt and Ice Beam are just two of its techniques.

HEIGHT:	3 ft 7 in
WEIGHT:	198 lb
TYPE:	WATER
ATTACKS:	SEA LION

#87 DEWGONG™

Dewgong stores thermal energy from the Sun in its body - and that's a lot of energy when you weigh a whopping 265 pounds! With its special Rest technique, Dewgong can bring itself back to full health!

HEIGHT:	5 ft 7 in
WEIGHT:	265 lb
TYPE:	WATER/ICE
ATTACKS:	SEA LION

#88 GRIMER™

This Pokémon can be used as a pollution-processing plant, because it loves sucking up polluted sludge that's pumped out of factories and gym lockers. Like Muk, Grimer likes dirt and slime, which is why it hangs around with Team Rocket!

HEIGHT:	2 ft 11 in
WEIGHT:	66 lb
TYPE:	POISON
ATTACKS:	SLUDGE

#89 MUK™

Keeping too many Muk and Grimer in one place can be a danger to your plumbing! Muk's body is so toxic, even its footprints are poisonous! Screech, Poison Gas and Disable are just a few techniques this Pokémon uses!

HEIGHT:	3 ft 11 in
WEIGHT:	66 lb
TYPE:	POISON
ATTACKS:	SLUDGE

#90 SHELLDER™

Shellder teases enemies by sticking out its tongue and spitting in their eyes! This Water Pokémon can use Leer, Ice Beam and several other attacks, but its hard shell is the best type of protection, because nothing gets past it!

HEIGHT:	1 ft
WEIGHT:	9 lb
TYPE:	WATER
ATTACKS:	BIVALVE

POKéMON™

#91 CLOYSTER™

HEIGHT:	4 ft 11 in
WEIGHT:	292 lb
TYPE:	WATER/ICE
ATTACKS:	BIVALVE

Cloyster uses its Spike Cannon technique to hit an enemy up to five times in a row! Its hard shell is so protective, that even a bomb couldn't force it open! That's why no one has ever managed to see its soft inner body!

#92 GASTLY™

Made of gas, Gastly is almost invisible. This Pokémon surrounds an enemy and puts it to sleep without it even noticing! Gastly and Haunter are part of a trio of poisonous Ghost Pokémon that cause havoc in the Pokémon Tower.

HEIGHT:	4 ft 3 in
WEIGHT:	0.2 lb
TYPE:	GHOST/POISON
ATTACKS:	GAS

#93 HAUNTER™

HEIGHT:	5 ft 3 in
WEIGHT:	0.2 lb
TYPE:	GHOST/POISON
ATTACKS:	GAS

Haunter and Gastly have a ghostly advantage over every other Pokémon – and they're almost impossible to attack! These Pokémon are a mystery, as no one knows if they're spooky spectres - or lonely Pokémon that want to play.

#94 GENGAR™

This mischievous Pokémon is a ghastly ghoul that gets a thrill out of scaring people. When there's a full Moon, Gengar pretends to be its enemy's shadow – then laughs at their fear! So Psychic, Grass and Bug Pokémon beware!

HEIGHT:	4 ft 11 in
WEIGHT:	89 lb
TYPE:	GHOST/POISON
ATTACKS:	SHADOW

#95 ONIX™

HEIGHT:	8 ft 10 in
WEIGHT:	463 lb
TYPE:	ROCK/GROUND
ATTACKS:	ROCK SNAKE

Onix is the longest Pokémon in existence. As it grows, the stone parts of its body turn black and become as hard as diamonds! With techniques like Rage, Slam, Tackle and Screech, this Pokémon is definitely not for a new trainer to take on!

#96 DROWZEE™

Drowzee's favourite attack is to put other Pokémon to sleep. Then it eats its opponents' dreams! But this Psychic Pokémon has to be careful, because only sweet dreams give it energy. Bad dreams make Drowzee sick!

HEIGHT:	3 ft 3 in
WEIGHT:	71 lb
TYPE:	PSYCHIC
ATTACKS:	HYPNOSIS

PR⬤FILES

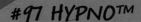

#97 HYPNO™

Hypno always carries a special pendant for hypnotising enemies, which gives out sleep waves. Hypno and Drowzee might not be the most powerful Pokémon, but their enemies won't be in any fit shape to fight back!

HEIGHT:	5 ft 3 in
WEIGHT:	167 lb
TYPE:	PSYCHIC
ATTACKS:	HYPNOSIS

#98 KRABBY™

Krabby can be very bad-tempered and will attack anything that invades their territory! These common river crabs use their strong pincers for balance when walking sideways – and as weapons to fend off attackers!

HEIGHT:	1 ft 4 in
WEIGHT:	14 lb
TYPE:	WATER
ATTACKS:	RIVER CRAB

#99 KINGLER™

Kingler can crush solid steel in its claws! It prefers the ocean to lakes and streams, because there's more prey to catch! Kingler and Krabby share the Guillotine move, which can automatically defeat an opponent.

HEIGHT:	4 ft 3 in
WEIGHT:	132 lb
TYPE:	WATER
ATTACKS:	PINCER CRAB

#100 VOLTORB™

Using its Screech technique to lower an enemy's defences, Voltorb then zaps it with an electric charge! If it thinks it's going to lose a battle, this fearsome Pokémon self-destructs. Until you pick it up, you won't know if you've got a Voltorb or a Poké Ball! So be very careful!

HEIGHT:	1 ft 8 in
WEIGHT:	23 lb
TYPE:	ELECTRIC
ATTACKS:	BALL

#101 ELECTRODE™

This Pokémon is full of electrical power, which it stores under very high pressure. For no reason at all, Electrode will often explode! This ball of electricity also uses techniques like Swift, Sonic Boom, Light Screen and Tackle to attack.

HEIGHT:	3 ft 11 in
WEIGHT:	147 lb
TYPE:	ELECTRIC
ATTACKS:	BALL

#102 EXEGGCUTE™

Exeggcute travel in swarms. When disturbed, they surround and attack any intruder in their territory. Did you know that every Pokémon has the Struggle ability, which can do some damage to an opponent?

HEIGHT:	1 ft 4 in
WEIGHT:	6 lb
TYPE:	GRASS/PSYCHIC
ATTACKS:	EGG

POKÉMON™

#103 EXEGGUTOR™

HEIGHT:	6 ft 7 in
WEIGHT:	265 lb
TYPE:	GRASS/PSYCHIC
ATTACKS:	COCONUT

Exeggutor is a three-headed coconut Pokémon. Each 'face' is different and has a distinct personality. Rumour has it that, occasionally, one of Exeggutor's 'heads' will fall off and start again as an Exeggcute.

#104 CUBONE™

This Pokémon never takes off its skull helmet, so nobody knows what it really looks like! Cubone uses bones of ancient Pokémon to make armour and weapons to fight with, and has fearsome Bonemerang and Thrash techniques!

HEIGHT:	1 ft 4 in
WEIGHT:	14 lb
TYPE:	GROUND
ATTACKS:	LONELY

#105 MAROWAK™

HEIGHT:	3 ft 3 in
WEIGHT:	99 lb
TYPE:	GROUND
ATTACKS:	BONE KEEPER

The bone that this Pokémon holds is its main weapon, which it throws like a boomerang. Legend has it that an angry Marowak haunts Pokémon Tower. Defeat it in battle – and its spirit will finally be at peace.

#106 HITMONLEE™

Hitmonlee and Hitmonchan work out at the gym of the Karate Master. If you defeat the Karate Master in battle, he might give you a Hitmonlee or a Hitmonchan! To increase its attack power, this Pokémon will Meditate.

HEIGHT:	4 ft 11 in
WEIGHT:	110 lb
TYPE:	FIGHTING
ATTACKS:	KICKING

#107 HITMONCHAN™

HEIGHT:	4 ft 7 in
WEIGHT:	111 lb
TYPE:	FIGHTING
ATTACKS:	PUNCHING

With punches faster than the speed of light, it's not a good idea to get Hitmonchan in a bad mood! It may not look like it's doing much, but your Pokémon will feel Hitmonchan's punches before it even sees them!

#108 LICKITUNG™

Lickitung can daze and confuse an enemy with its Wrap technique – then attack up to five times in a row with the Supersonic! After just one lick, this Pokémon's tongue leaves an opponent tingling all over.

HEIGHT:	3 ft 11 in
WEIGHT:	144 lb
TYPE:	NORMAL
ATTACKS:	LICKING

PROFILES

#109 KOFFING™

Koffing stores several kinds of toxic gas in its body at once. Unfortunately, this rotten combination of gases often makes it explode without warning! If you're allergic to toxic fumes, this isn't a good Pokémon to carry around!

HEIGHT:	2 ft
WEIGHT:	2 lb
TYPE:	POISON
ATTACKS:	POISON GAS

#110 WEEZING™

Weezing is much heavier and more solid than Koffing – and that's because it's made up of toxic liquids instead of gases. When two types of poisonous gas meet, Koffing will change into a Weezing Pokémon.

HEIGHT:	3 ft 11 in
WEIGHT:	21 lb
TYPE:	POISON
ATTACKS:	POISON GAS

#111 RHYHORN™

This Pokémon can take on even the fiercest attackers – and that's because its bones are one thousand times stronger than human bones! This unbelievably strong Pokémon can throw a school bus over its shoulder!

HEIGHT:	3 ft 3 in
WEIGHT:	254 lb
TYPE:	GROUND/ROCK
ATTACKS:	SPIKES

#112 RHYDON™

Rhydon's Take Down technique is like getting hit with a tank! It lives deep underground in molten lava that reaches over 3,600 degrees! Rhydon's hard skin protects it from the extreme heat and pressure beneath the earth.

HEIGHT:	6 ft 3 in
WEIGHT:	265 lb
TYPE:	GROUND/ROCK
ATTACKS:	DRILL

#113 CHANSEY™

These Pokémon are hard to find, but make excellent friends. Their magical powers bring happiness to any trainer who is lucky enough to capture one. You can find Chansey in most Pokémon centres taking care of sick Pokémon.

HEIGHT:	3 ft 7 in
WEIGHT:	76 lb
TYPE:	NORMAL
ATTACKS:	EGG

#114 TANGELA™

Tangela has a great Sleep Powder technique! Covered in seaweed-like vines that shake as it walks, you may find a rare Tangela in a patch of thick grass south of Pallet Town. But you'll have to search hard, as it is very shy.

HEIGHT:	3 ft 3 in
WEIGHT:	77 lb
TYPE:	GRASS
ATTACKS:	VINE

HEIGHT:	7 ft 3 in
WEIGHT:	176 lb
TYPE:	NORMAL
ATTACKS:	PARENT

#115 KANGASKHAN™

This Pokémon attacks without warning if it thinks its infant, carried in a special stomach pouch, is in any danger. At one time, Kangaskhan were almost extinct. Fortunately, they are now protected by law and live within the Safari Zone.

#116 HORSEA™

Horsea Pokémon have been known to shoot down bugs from the surface of the water with blasts of ink. But although they have good defence techniques, Horsea are fragile and can't handle too many major attacks.

HEIGHT:	1 ft 4 in
WEIGHT:	18 lb
TYPE:	WATER
ATTACKS:	DRAGON

HEIGHT:	3 ft 11 in
WEIGHT:	55 lb
TYPE:	WATER
ATTACKS:	DRAGON

#117 SEADRA™

These Pokémon use their spiky fins to pierce an enemy's skin! But there's no such thing as a 'bad' Pokémon – masters command their Pokémon to do bad things. Meowth, a member of Team Rocket, is the only exception!

#118 GOLDEEN™

Goldeen's rippled tail fins flow like an elegant gown, but don't be fooled by its beauty. Goldeen can call upon techniques that would worry quite a few Pokémon; Agility, Supersonic, Horn and Fury Attack are just some!

HEIGHT:	2 ft 3 in
WEIGHT:	33 lb
TYPE:	WATER
ATTACKS:	GOLDFISH

HEIGHT:	4 ft 3 in
WEIGHT:	86 lb
TYPE:	WATER
ATTACKS:	GOLDFISH

#119 SEAKING™

This Pokémon swims powerfully up rivers and creeks for the spawning season, which is in the autumn. As Goldeen evolves into Seaking, its horn skill increases. Fire, Ground and Rock Pokémon need to watch this gigantic goldfish!

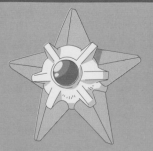

#120 STARYU™

Staryu uses its psychic powers to move around and can easily regrow any of the starry points it may lose in battle, too! This mysterious Pokémon uses Mirage to improve its chances of avoiding an attack.

HEIGHT:	2 ft 7 in
WEIGHT:	276 lb
TYPE:	WATER
ATTACKS:	STAR SHAPE

PROFILES

#121 STARMIE™

HEIGHT: 3 ft 7 in
WEIGHT: 176 lb
TYPE: WATER/PSYCHIC
ATTACKS: STAR SHAPE

Starmie is one of Misty's favourite Pokémon to use in battle. Although it can't move quickly, its many-sided skin gives it protection. Starmie has a jewel at its centre that glows with the seven colours of the rainbow - and is very valuable.

#122 Mr. MIME™

If provoked, Mr. Mime will slap an enemy with its large hands. With its Substitute technique, this Pokémon can make more than one copy of itself - and each 'copy' shares one quarter of the original Mr. Mime's energy!

HEIGHT: 4 ft 3 in
WEIGHT: 120 lb
TYPE: PSYCHIC
ATTACKS: BARRIER

#123 SCYTHER™

HEIGHT: 4 ft 11 in
WEIGHT: 123 lb
TYPE: BUG/FLYING
ATTACKS: MANTIS

It looks more like a dinosaur than a Bug Pokémon, but Scyther's razor-edged wings make its Slash technique a killer! Add to that its Agility, Leer and Swords Dance techniques and an enemy doesn't stand a chance!

#124 JYNX™

Jynx can wiggle its hips - and make others dance along with it! In Cerulean City, there's a man who will trade a common Poliwhirl for this rare and strange-looking Pokémon. Look out for Jynx's Lovely Kiss technique!

HEIGHT: 4 ft 7 in
WEIGHT: 90 lb
TYPE: ICE/PSYCHIC
ATTACKS: HUMAN SHAPE

#125 ELECTABUZZ™

HEIGHT: 3 ft 7 in
WEIGHT: 66 lb
TYPE: ELECTRIC
ATTACKS: ELECTRIC

These Pokémon are attracted to strong sources of energy, so it's hardly surprising that they're usually found near power plants. But if Electabuzz wander off, they can cause blackouts in major cities!

#126 MAGMAR™

Magmar is hard to spot in a fire. Its body burns steadily with a bright orange glow, blending in perfectly with the flames. But it's not too 'hot' when up against Fire, Water, Rock or Dragon Pokémon!

HEIGHT: 4 ft 3 in
WEIGHT: 98 lb
TYPE: FIRE
ATTACKS: FLAME

#127 PINSIR™

HEIGHT:	4 ft 1 in
WEIGHT:	121 lb
TYPE:	BUG
ATTACKS:	STAG BEETLE

Pinsir relies on its strength and huge pincers to win a battle. If it can't crush an enemy in its claws, Pinsir swings it around its head - and throws hard! This stag beetle has techniques that will make your Pokémon faint with fright!

#128 TAUROS™

Tauros can be very difficult to control, even for an advanced trainer. This Pokémon charges violently as it whips enemies with its long tails. It also uses some scary Stomp, Leer, Tackle, Take Down and Rage techniques!

HEIGHT:	4 ft 7 in
WEIGHT:	195 lb
TYPE:	NORMAL
ATTACKS:	WILD BULL

#129 MAGIKARP™

HEIGHT:	2 ft 11 in
WEIGHT:	22 lb
TYPE:	WATER
ATTACKS:	FISH

With Splash and Tackle as its only techniques this is one of the weaker Pokémon. You can fish for a Magikarp almost anywhere and start training it immediately for evolution. When it evolves into Gyarados, this Water Pokémon will be very strong.

#130 GYARADOS™

Gyarados has a terrible temper. Its fangs can crush stones and its scales are harder than steel! If Gyarados gets angry, it will destroy a city. This snake-like Pokémon's Dragon Rage technique can cause typhoons and sea storms.

HEIGHT:	21 ft 4 in
WEIGHT:	518 lb
TYPE:	WATER/FLYING
ATTACKS:	ATROCIOUS

#131 LAPRAS™

HEIGHT:	8 ft 2 in
WEIGHT:	485 lb
TYPE:	WATER/ICE
ATTACKS:	TRANSPORT

This gentle, good-natured Pokémon is now almost extinct. But it happily carries passengers across small bodies of water. Although Lapras weighs 485 pounds, Snorlax is over twice that weight, at a gargantuan 1,014 pounds!

#132 DITTO™

This Pokémon has the ability to copy an enemy's DNA – or genetic code. Then it rearranges its own cells and instantly turns into a mirror image of its enemy! Transform is Ditto's only technique, but it's all it needs.

HEIGHT:	1 ft
WEIGHT:	9 lb
TYPE:	NORMAL
ATTACKS:	TRANSFORM

PROFILES

#133 EEVEE™

HEIGHT:	1 ft
WEIGHT:	14 lb
TYPE:	NORMAL
ATTACKS:	EVOLUTION

Eevee doesn't evolve on its own like other Pokémon. There are three special stones – Water, Thunder and Fire, that can trigger a change in this Pokémon – and each stone turns Eevee into a different kind of Pokémon.

#134 VAPOREON™

The Water Stone turns Eevee into Vaporeon, which has a long, beautiful tail, edged with a fin. This Pokémon can melt into water and make itself disappear. Watch out for its Water Gun, Bite and Hydro Pump attacks!

HEIGHT: 3 ft 3 in
WEIGHT: 64 lb
TYPE: WATER
ATTACKS: BUBBLE JET

#135 JOLTEON™

HEIGHT:	2 ft 7 in
WEIGHT:	54 lb
TYPE:	ELECTRIC
ATTACKS:	LIGHTNING

With the use of a Thunder Stone, Jolteon has evolved from Eevee. Collecting negatively charged atoms from the atmosphere, this Electric Pokémon uses them to throw out 10,000 volts of lightning!

#136 FLAREON™

Flareon has changed from Eevee with the use of a Fire Stone. Storing thermal energy from the Sun in its body, this Pokémon's temperature can rise to over 1,600 degrees! Using its blazing Fire technique, Flareon is very strong.

HEIGHT:	2 ft 1 in
WEIGHT:	55 lb
TYPE:	FIRE
ATTACKS:	FLAME

#137 PORYGON™

HEIGHT:	2 ft 7 in
WEIGHT:	80 lb
TYPE:	NORMAL
ATTACKS:	VIRTUAL

Porygon lives in cyberspace. Its crystal-like body is computer-generated, which means that it's made up of computer code, like a video game character. Some collectors would rather show off Porygon than use it in battle.

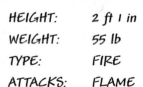

#138 OMANYTE™

Omanyte has been extinct for thousands of years, but scientists can now bring this Pokémon back to life! You'll need to take a Helix Fossil to the Pokémon Laboratory on Cinnabar Island, where scientists will make a living Omanyte.

HEIGHT: 1 ft 4 in
WEIGHT: 17 lb
TYPE: ROCK/WATER
ATTACKS: S PIRAL

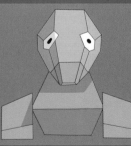

POKÉMON™

#139 OMASTAR™

This Pokémon is a scientific mystery! Some people believe that Omastar died out when its heavy shell made it impossible for it to catch food. You can get a Helix Fossil to make an Omanyte, by defeating a rival Pokémon trainer on Mt. Moon!

HEIGHT:	3 ft 3 in
WEIGHT:	77 lb
TYPE:	ROCK/WATER
ATTACKS:	SPIRAL

#140 KABUTO™

To get one of these beetle-like Pokémon, you need to get a Dome Fossil by defeating a rival trainer on Mt. Moon. Then take the fossil to the scientists on Cinnabar Island – and they'll revive your Kabuto.

HEIGHT:	1 ft 8 in
WEIGHT:	25 lb
TYPE:	ROCK/WATER
ATTACKS:	SHELLFISH

#141 KABUTOPS™

Kabutops has extremely long, sharp claws that it uses to attack opponents. Its sleek shape makes it a perfect swimmer. This shellfish Pokémon uses Scratch, Slash and Hydro Pump techniques to defend itself.

HEIGHT:	4 ft 3 in
WEIGHT:	89 lb
TYPE:	ROCK/WATER
ATTACKS:	SHELLFISH

#142 AERODACTYL™

This Pokémon can't be captured in the wild. It must be 'cloned' in the Pokémon laboratory using old amber from the Pewter City Museum. Aerodactyl's sharp, saw-like fangs can cause a lot of damage to an enemy.

HEIGHT:	5 ft 11 in
WEIGHT:	130 lb
TYPE:	ROCK/FLYING
ATTACKS:	FOSSIL

#143 SNORLAX™

Sleeping and eating is this Pokémon's favourite pastime! The bigger Snorlax gets, the sleepier it becomes - so it's probably best not to feed it too much. Beware of this lazy lump of blubber's Body Slam technique!

HEIGHT:	6 ft 11 in
WEIGHT:	1014 lb
TYPE:	NORMAL
ATTACKS:	SLEEPING

#144 ARTICUNO™

Articuno is part of a trio, along with Zapdos and Moltres. It lives at the bottom of a cavern where the current is strongest on the Seafoam Islands. To catch this rare Pokémon, a Poké Ball won't be enough! You will need lots of Ultra Balls.

HEIGHT:	5 ft 7 in
WEIGHT:	122 lb
TYPE:	ICE/FLYING
ATTACKS:	FREEZE

PRFILES

#145 ZAPDOS™

HEIGHT:	5 ft 3 in
WEIGHT:	116 lb
TYPE:	ELECTRIC/FLYING
ATTACKS:	ELECTRIC

Zapdos, the second legendary bird, appears from the clouds while blasting bolts of lightning – or so legend says! Its Light Screen defence reduces by half the amount of damage it receives from other attacks.

#146 MOLTRES™

This Pokémon is seen so rarely, that people think it isn't real. Each flap of its wings creates a display of flames. Some Pokémon are so rare, they're one of a kind, like Articuno, Zapdos, Moltres, Mewtwo, Eevee and Farfetch'd.

HEIGHT:	6 ft 7 in
WEIGHT:	132 lb
TYPE:	FIRE/FLYING
ATTACKS:	FLAME

#147 DRATINI™

HEIGHT:	5 ft 11 in
WEIGHT:	7 lb
TYPE:	DRAGON
ATTACKS:	DRAGON

Dratini were thought to be only mythical Pokémon. But a small colony has been discovered living deep under the water. These Dragon Pokémon have some very useful battle techniques like Wrap and Leer.

#148 DRAGONAIR™

Dragonair is so gentle, even the air around it feels calm. This Pokémon also has the ability to change the weather! Most of its dragon techniques like Wrap, Agility and Dragon Rage make use of Dragonair's long and powerful body.

HEIGHT:	13 ft 1 in
WEIGHT:	36 lb
TYPE:	DRAGON
ATTACKS:	DRAGON

#149 DRAGONITE™

HEIGHT:	7 ft 3 in
WEIGHT:	463 lb
TYPE:	DRAGON/FLYING
ATTACKS:	DRAGON

As water dwellers, Dragonite are hardly ever seen. Said to be as bright as humans, their ancestors were probably the winged dragons of fairy tales. Dragonite aren't very good against Electric or Rock Pokémon.

#150 MEWTWO™

This is the most difficult Pokémon to capture! Genetically engineered, Mewtwo is very hostile. To catch it, you'll need a Master Ball. If you defeat Mewtwo, you will be worthy of the title 'The World's Greatest Pokémon Master'!

HEIGHT:	6 ft 7 in
WEIGHT:	269 lb
TYPE:	PSYCHIC
ATTACKS:	GENETIC

Pokémon
Gotta catch 'em all!

HERE COMES THE SQUIRTLE SQUAD!

Ash was telling Misty and Brock how lucky he was to have gained a Charmander to go with his Pikachu and Bulbasaur, when suddenly the friends fell into a hole!

"Squirtle!" said a Pokémon, as Ash looked out of the hole.

"Squirtle! This tiny turtle Pokémon draws its long neck into its shell to launch water attacks with amazing range and accuracy. The blast can be quite powerful!" announced Ash's Pokédex.

"With my own Squirtle, Professor Oak's grandson will never beat me!" said Ash. "Go, Pikachu!"

As Pikachu fired its Thundershock attack, the weakened Squirtle fell.

Suddenly, other Squirtle appeared and carried the injured Pokémon away.

"Has anyone been hurt?" said a girl, pulling up on her motorbike.

"Officer Jenny!" said Ash. "We met you back in Viridian City!"

"You mean you met one of the other 'Jenny's'!" said the girl. "My cousins are all police officers. We're all identical – and we're all called Jenny!"

Jenny then explained that the Pokémon

they had just seen called themselves 'The Squirtle Squad'. They had all been deserted by their Pokémon trainers and ran wild, playing tricks on the whole town!

"If they had had someone to care about them, they wouldn't have turned out to be as bad as they are," said Jenny.

From a nearby hill, Team Rocket were so busy watching Ash and his friends, they didn't notice the Squirtle Squad surround them!

"Squirtle! Squirtle! Squirtle!" said the Pokémon.

"Meowth, what are they saying?" asked Jessie.

"They're saying, 'give us your food, or else!'" said Meowth.

Jessie and James swung round to go after the Squirtle – and fell down a hole instead!

The Squirtle lost no time! They tied up Jessie, James and Meowth – then ate all their food!

"Ask the Squirtle if they will help us capture three kids and their Pikachu – and tell them our boss will make it worth their while!" said Jessie.

"No deal! The Squirtle don't trust humans," said Meowth.

"Then make them trust us!" hissed James.

"Squirtle, these humans are my pets. I trained them, but they're pretty stupid," said Meowth in Squirtle language.

At last, the Squirtle Squad untied Meowth, who then ate the rest of the food!

HERE COMES THE SQUIRTLE SQUAD!

Meanwhile, Ash, Misty and Brock were fishing when a Squirtle shot out of the water and attacked them with its Hydro Pump technique!

As water sprayed over Pikachu, it caused an electric current to shoot through the air!

"Wet clothes conduct electricity!" gasped Brock, as he and Ash fell on to the grass.

When the Squirtle came out of the water, it used its Tackle technique to send Pikachu hurtling into the river!

Pikachu tried to reach safety, but a Goldeen Pokémon swam up and used its Horn Attack to knock Pikachu out of the water!

Then, with a surprise attack, Squirtle tied Ash, Misty and Brock together.

"I'm the Pokémon in charge here!" said Meowth, when the trainers were taken to a cave. "Just wait until my pet humans get back!"

"Don't believe Meowth!" said Ash. "Team Rocket are trying to trick you into doing their dirty work!"

"Pikachu's in bad shape," said Misty.

"We've got to heal Pikachu with Super Potion before it's too late!" said Brock.

"There's a shop in town that sells it."

"Squirtle, you've got to let me go into town!" begged Ash.

The Squirtle shook their heads.

"As soon as I buy the medicine, I'll come back," said Ash, a tear trickling down his face.

At last, the Squirtle Squad showed some sympathy and released Ash.

"The Squirtle Squad say that if you're not back by noon tomorrow, the red-headed girl gets her hair dyed purple!" said Meowth.

Ash ran and ran, until he reached an old bridge. But as he tried to cross it, the wooden slats broke – and Ash plummeted into the water, where a Goldeen used its Horn Attack to send him flying back into the air!

Injured, Ash limped to town. But just as he was about to go into the shop, the door swung open – and knocked him out cold!

Next morning, Ash woke to hear Jessie and James inside the shop!

"Everybody freeze! These are ice packs we're gunning," stammered James. "I mean, ice guns we're packing!"

"We want all the Flash Powder you've got!" said Jessie, sure that the powder would scare the Squirtle Squad out of town.

As Team Rocket left, Ash knew he had to get back to the cave before they did.

HERE COMES THE SQUIRTLE SQUAD!

"Super Potion, please!" said Ash, running into the shop.

But the customers had been bullied enough for one day and they wouldn't listen!

Officer Jenny showed up just in time to explain to everyone that Ash wasn't a member of Team Rocket.

"Hang on, Ash!" said Jenny as they sped off on her motorbike – with Pikachu's Super Potion.

"These flash blasts will scare those Squirtle!" laughed James, as he and Jessie prepared to do battle.

"In all the confusion, we'll snatch Pikachu!" said Jessie.

Reaching the entrance to the cave, Jenny told Ash he would have to go in alone, as the opening was too small for an adult.

The cave was very dark and Ash couldn't see where he was going. Then he had an idea!

Taking out a Poké Ball, Ash said, "Charmander! I choose you!"

Its tail glowing, Charmander lit the way. But the cave was empty!

"We're here!" called Misty, as Ash ran outside.

Just as Ash sprayed Super Potion on

Pikachu, there was a loud blast.

Hovering overhead, Jessie and James threw down several blast balls.

As rocks tumbled around them, everyone headed for the cave. But one Squirtle had been injured.

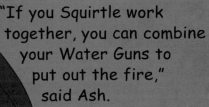

As another blast rang out, Ash ran back and covered the Squirtle to protect it.

Encouraged by Ash's bravery, the Squirtle summoned up the last of its strength, picked up Ash – and ran towards the cave!

"No more Squirtle Squad!" laughed Jessie, thinking they had all been injured. "The town is going to give us medals and we'll be heroes!"

"Not so fast!" said Ash.

"Who said that?" gasped Jessie.

"Huh! How did they?!" said James.

"Squirtle! Water Gun attack now!" called Ash.

One blast of water sent the balloon spinning through the air.

As Team Rocket disappeared into the distance, Brock said, "There's a fire! The blast must have set it off!"

"If it keeps burning, the whole town could go up in smoke!" said Officer Jenny.

"If you Squirtle work together, you can combine your Water Guns to put out the fire," said Ash.

The Squirtle did as they had been asked and quickly put out the fire.

Later, as everyone in the town clapped, Officer Jenny said, "We award this certificate to the Squirtle Squad. Because of your skill and bravery, we proudly appoint you the town fire fighters!"

As the Pokémon trainers set off on another adventure, Misty noticed something. "That Squirtle is following us!" she whispered.

"Would you like to come with us, Squirtle?" asked Ash.

"Squirtle!" replied the Squirtle.

"Welcome to the team!" laughed Ash. "I guess I've got a new Pokémon!"

Use your crayons to colour this picture of Ash and his Pokémon friend, Pikachu.